the source

arrangements for worship groups

book 1

B♭ instruments

arranged by Chris Mitchell

Kevin Mayhew

We hope you enjoy the music in this book.
Further copies of this and the other books in the series are available
from your local music shop or Christian bookshop.

In case of difficulty, please contact the publisher direct:

The Sales Department
KEVIN MAYHEW LTD
Rattlesden
Bury St Edmunds
Suffolk IP30 0SZ

Phone 01449 737978
Fax 01449 737834

Please ask for our complete catalogue of outstanding Church Music.

the source will be developed into a major resource for
the churches. It is already available in the following editions

Words Only	ISBN	1 84003 121 2
	Catalogue No.	1470101
Full Music	ISBN	1 84003 120 4
	Catalogue No.	1470104
Complete Acetate Masters	ISBN	1 84003 119 0
	Catalogue No.	1470201

First published in Great Britain in 1998 by Kevin Mayhew Ltd.

© Copyright 1998 Kevin Mayhew Ltd.

ISBN 1 84003 128 X
ISMN M 57004 211 1
Catalogue No: 1470307

0 1 2 3 4 5 6 7 8 9

Cover designed by Jaquetta Sergeant

Music arrangements by Chris Mitchell
Music Editor: Donald Thomson
Music setting by Lynwen Davies and Chris Mitchell

Printed and bound in Great Britain by
Caligraving Limited Thetford Norfolk

Contents

This index gives the first line of each hymn. If a hymn is known by an alternative title, this is also given, but indented and in italics.

	No.		No.
Abba, Father, let me be	1	Before the world began	40
Abide with me	2	Be free	41
Above the clash of creeds	3	Be glorified	42
Alleluia, alleluia, give thanks to the risen Lord	4	Behold his love	43
All hail King Jesus!	5	Behold the Lord	44
All hail the Lamb	6	Beneath the cross of Jesus	45
All hail the power of Jesus' name	7	Be patient, be ready	46
All heaven declares	8	Be still, for the presence of the Lord	47
All heaven waits	9	Be still and know	48
All honour, all glory	10	Be still, my soul	49
All I once held dear	11	Be thou my vision	50
All over the world	12	Bind us together	51
All people that on earth do dwell	13	Blessed assurance, Jesus is mine	52
All things bright and beautiful	14	*Blessed be the Lord God Almighty*	96
All things are possible	17	Blessed be the name of the Lord	53
All to Jesus I surrender	15	Blessing and honour	54
Almighty God, we bring you praise	16	Blessing, honour, glory to the Lamb	55
Almighty God, my Redeemer	17	Bless the Lord, my soul	56
Amazing grace	18	Breathe on me, Breath of God	57
Among the gods	19	Broken for me	58
An army of ordinary people	20	By his grace	59
Ancient of Days	54	By your side	60
And can it be	21	Called to a battle	61
And he shall reign	22	Can a nation be changed?	62
A new commandment	23	Can I ascend	63
Anointing, fall on me	24	Can we walk upon the water	64
Ascribe greatness	25	Can you see what we have made	65
As I come into your presence	26	*Celebrate*	75
As the deer pants (Nystrom)	27	Celebrate, celebrate	66
As the deer pants (Lewis)	28	Celebrate Jesus	67
As we are gathered	29	Change my heart, O God	68
As we lift up your name	30	Colours of day	69
As we seek your face	31	Come and see	70
At the foot of the cross	32	Come down, O Love divine	71
At the name of Jesus	33	Come, let us return	72
At this time of giving	34	Come, let us worship Jesus	73
At your feet we fall	35	Come on, all us singers, sing	74
Away in a manger	36	Come on and celebrate	75
Awesome in this place	26	Come, Spirit, come	76
Beauty for brokenness	37	Crown him with many crowns	77
Be bold, be strong	38	Day of favour	78
Because of your love	39	Dear Lord and Father of mankind	79

	No.		No.
Did you feel the mountains tremble?	80	*I will sing your praises*	91
Don't let my love grow cold	81	*King of the nations*	73
Do something new, Lord	82	*Knowing you*	11
Down the mountain the river flows	83	*Let forgiveness flow*	94
Draw me closer	84	*Let the peace of God reign*	100
Earth lies spellbound	85	*Let your glory fall*	99
Every nation, power and tongue	86	*Light the fire again*	81
Exalt the Lord	87	*Light up the fire*	69
Faithful God	88	*No other way*	3
Faithful One	89	*People just like us*	86
Far and near	90	*Revival fire, fall*	30
Father God, I wonder	91	*Say it loud*	90
Father God, we worship you	92	*Seven reasons to celebrate*	66
Father, hear our prayer	93	*Singers' song*	74
Father, here I am	94	*Song for Christingle*	65
Father, I come to you	95	*So you would come*	40
Father in heaven, how we love you	96	*The giving song*	34
Father, I place into your hands	97	*The river is here*	83
Father, I want you to hold me	98	*Thunder in the skies*	61
Father of creation	99	*Unending love*	95
Father of life, draw me closer	100	*We worship at your feet*	70
Glory to the Lamb	55	*White horse*	46
God of the poor	37	*You alone are God*	19
I'm coming up the mountain	63	*Your waves of love*	28
I surrender all	15		

CHRIS MITCHELL is a well-established arranger, composer, musical director and session musician who has worked with Graham Kendrick, David Peacock, Gloria Gaynor and the BBC. He and his wife, Linda, are experienced worship leaders and are involved in providing seminars and workshops for Christians in the arts.

1 Abba, Father, let me be

Dave Bilbrough

2 Abide with me

William Henry Monk

5 verses

3 Above the clash of creeds
(No other way)

Graham Kendrick

4 Alleluia, alleluia, give thanks to the risen Lord

Donald Fishel

5 All hail King Jesus!

Dave Moody

Worshipfully with strength

6 All hail the Lamb

Dave Bilbrough

With awe

7 All hail the power of Jesus' name (Tune 1)

William Shrubsole

6 verses

7a All hail the power of Jesus' name (Tune 2)

James Ellor

6 verses

8 All heaven declares

Noel and Tricia Richards

2 verses

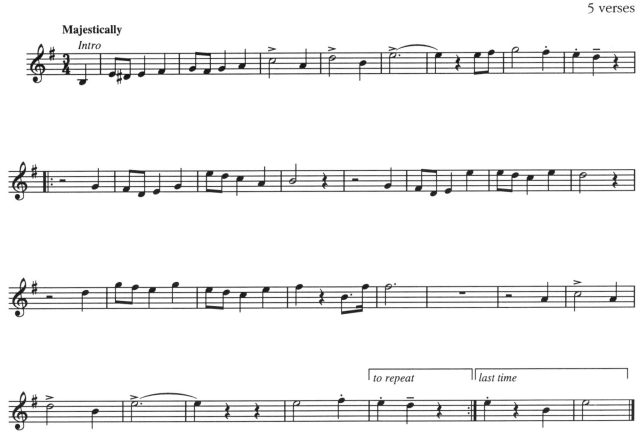

9 All heaven waits

Graham Kendrick

5 verses

10 All honour, all glory

Chris Falson

11 All I once held dear

(Knowing you)

Graham Kendrick   3 verses

Smoothly
Verse

Chorus

12 All over the world

Terry Butler

2 verses

13 All people that on earth do dwell

From the *Genevan Psalter*

5 verses

14 All things bright and beautiful (Tune 1)

Traditional English melody

4 verses

14a All things bright and beautiful (Tune 2)

William Henry Monk

4 verses

15 All to Jesus I surrender
(I surrender all)

W.S. Weedon

5 verses

16 Almighty God, we bring you praise

Austin Martin

17 Almighty God, my Redeemer
(All things are possible)
Darlene Zschech

18 Amazing grace

American folk melody

6 verses

19 Among the gods
(You alone are God)

Carol Owen

20 An army of ordinary people

Dave Bilbrough

2 verses

With feeling

21 And can it be

Thomas Campbell

5 verses

22 And he shall reign

Graham Kendrick

3 verses

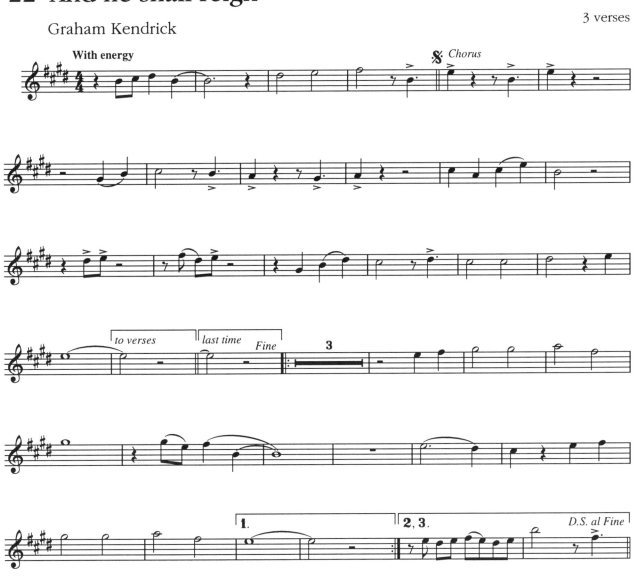

23 A new commandment

Unknown

24 Anointing, fall on me

Donn Charles Thomas

25 Ascribe greatness

Peter West, Mary Lou Locke and Mary Kirkbride

26 As I come into your presence

(Awesome in this place)

Dave Billington

27 As the deer pants

Martin J. Nystrom

3 verses

28 As the deer pants
(Your waves of love)

Richard Lewis

29 As we are gathered

John Daniels

30 As we lift up your name
(Revival fire, fall)

2 verses

Paul Baloche

31 As we seek your face

Dave Bilbrough

3 verses

32 At the foot of the cross

Derek Bond

With a gentle rhythm

33 At the name of Jesus

Michael Brierley

7 verses

34 At this time of giving
(The giving song)

Graham Kendrick

3 verses

35 At your feet we fall

David Fellingham

3 verses

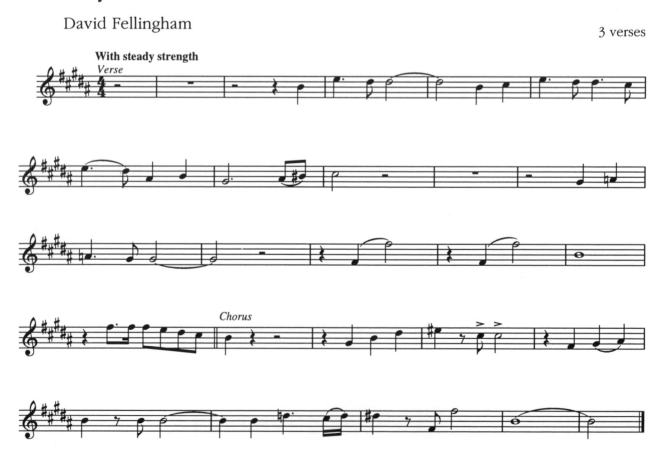

36 Away in a manger

William James Kirkpatrick

3 verses

37 Beauty for brokenness
(God of the poor)

Graham Kendrick

5 verses

38 Be bold, be strong

Morris Chapman

39 Because of your love

Russell Fragar

40 Before the world began
(So you would come)

Russell Fragar

41 Be free

Dave Bilbrough

2 verses

42 Be glorified

Billy Funk

43 Behold his love

Geoff Baker

44 Behold the Lord

Noel Richards and Gerald Coates

3 verses

45 Beneath the cross of Jesus

5 verses

Frederick C. Maker

46 Be patient, be ready
(White horse)

Graham Kendrick

47 Be still, for the presence of the Lord

David J. Evans

3 verses

48 Be still and know

Unknown

3 verses

49 Be still, my soul

Jean Sibelius

3 verses

50 Be thou my vision

Traditional Irish melody

5 verses

51 Bind us together

Bob Gillman

3 verses

52 Blessed assurance, Jesus is mine

Phoebe Palmer Knapp

3 verses

53 Blessed be the name of the Lord

Kevin Prosch and Danny Daniels

2 verses

54 Blessing and honour
(Ancient of Days)

Gary Sadler and Jamie Harvill

55 Blessing, honour, glory to the Lamb
(Glory to the Lamb)

Geoff Bullock and Dave Reidy

56 Bless the Lord, my soul

Jacques Berthier

57 Breathe on me, Breath of God (Tune 1)

Charles Lockhart

4 verses

57a Breathe on me, Breath of God (Tune 2)

Robert Jackson

4 verses

58 Broken for me

Janet Lunt

4 verses

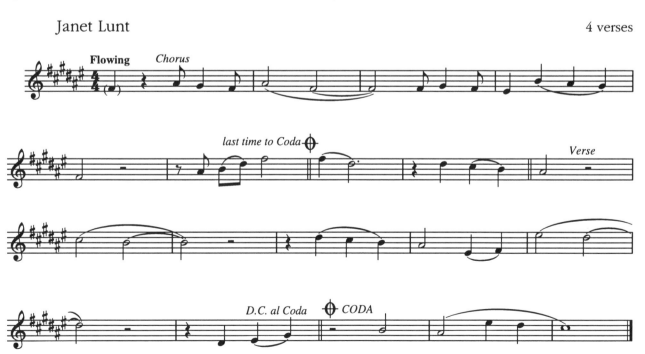

59 By his grace

Steven Fry

60 By your side

Noel and Tricia Richards

61 Called to a battle
(Thunder in the skies)

Noel and Tricia Richards

2 verses

62 Can a nation be changed?

Matt Redman

2 verses

63 Can I ascend
(I'm coming up the mountain)

Matt Redman

64 Can we walk upon the water

Matt Redman

2 verses

65 Can you see what we have made
(Song for Christingle)

Graham Kendrick

5 verses

66 Celebrate, celebrate
(Seven reasons to celebrate)

Graham Kendrick

67 Celebrate Jesus

Gary Oliver

68 Change my heart, O God

Eddie Espinosa

69 Colours of day
(Light up the fire)

Sue McClellan, John Paculabo and Keith Ryecroft

3 verses

70 Come and see
(We worship at your feet)

Graham Kendrick

3 verses

71 Come down, O Love divine

Ralph Vaughan Williams

4 verses

72 Come, let us return

Graham Kendrick

73 Come, let us worship Jesus
(King of the nations)

5 verses

Graham Kendrick

74 Come on, all us singers, sing
(Singers' song)

Martin Smith

75 Come on and celebrate

(Celebrate)

Patricia Morgan and Dave Bankhead

76 Come, Spirit, come

Elizabeth Bourbourze

3 verses

77 Crown him with many crowns

George Job Elvey

5 verses

78 Day of favour

David Fellingham

2 verses

79 Dear Lord and Father of mankind

Charles Hubert Hastings Parry

5 verses

80 Did you feel the mountains tremble?

Martin Smith

3 verses

81 Don't let my love grow cold
(Light the fire again)

Brian Doerksen

82 Do something new, Lord

Chris Bowater

3 verses

83 Down the mountain the river flows

(The river is here)

Andy Park

With joy

84 Draw me closer

Stuart Devane and Glenn Gore

Flowing

85 Earth lies spellbound

Graham Kendrick

3 verses

86 Every nation, power and tongue
(People just like us)

3 verses

Russell Fragar

87 Exalt the Lord

Mike and Claire McIntosh

88 Faithful God

Chris Bowater

Worshipfully and unhurried

89 Faithful One

Brian Doerksen

90 Far and near
(Say it loud)
Graham Kendrick

3 verses

91 Father God, I wonder
(I will sing your praises)
Ian Smale

92 Father God, we worship you

Graham Kendrick

3 verses

93 Father, hear our prayer

Andy Piercy

94 Father, here I am
(Let forgiveness flow)

Danny Daniels

95 Father, I come to you
(Unending love)

John Barnett

3 verses

96 Father in heaven, how we love you
(Blessed be the Lord God Almighty)

Bob Fitts

97 Father, I place into your hands

Jenny Hewer

4 verses

98 Father, I want you to hold me

Brian Doerksen

2 verses

99 Father of creation
(Let your glory fall)

David Ruis

2 verses

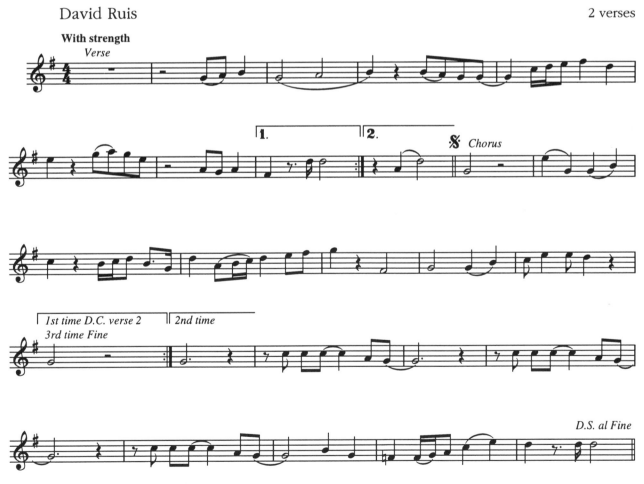

100 Father of life, draw me closer
(Let the peace of God reign)

Darlene Zschech